MISS GALAXY'S SPACE LESSONS

Pickle Hill Primary

Mr Day's Knight Lessons
Phil Roxbee Cox

Miss Scorcher's Desert Lessons
Valerie Wilding

Mr Megamouth's Shark Lessons
Micheal Cox

PICKLE HILL PRIMARY
WHERE ANYTHING CAN HAPPEN

MISS GALAXY'S SPACE LESSONS

Phil Roxbee Cox

illustrated by
Kelly Waldek

■SCHOLASTIC

For my wife, the centre of my universe

Scholastic Children's Books,
Commonwealth House,
1-19 New Oxford Street,
London WC1A

A division of Scholastic Ltd
London ~ New York ~ Toronto ~ Sydney ~ Auckland
Mexico City ~ New Delhi ~ Hong Kong

Published in the UK by Scholastic Ltd, 2002

ISBN 0 439 99432 2

Typeset by Goodfellow & Egan Ltd, Cambridge
Printed by Cox & Wyman Ltd, Reading, Berks

1 3 5 7 9 10 8 6 4 2

Contents

WELCOME TO PICKLE HILL PRIMARY

I'm Bernie Roberts, official class joker in class 5B. It's my job to make sure that we all have a good laugh, which isn't hard in a school like Pickle Hill Primary... except that there isn't another school LIKE Pickle Hill Primary. It's as unusual as a tap-dancing elephant!

You should see our teachers — the things that they get up to and the things they can do. In this book, Miss Galaxy teaches us about stars and planets, and moons and meteors and that kind of stuff. But it's HOW she teaches us that's so brilliant.

One minute, the whole classroom might be launching out of Earth's orbit, and the next? You might find yourself being sucked out of your seat and into a black hole that's appeared on the board!!!

Don't believe me? Then join me and the rest of 5B for Miss Galaxy's space lessons!

by **Bernie Roberts**

PICKLE HILL PRIMARY

Teacher's Name: Miss Galaxy

Age: **38** (so she says)

Appearance: Planet-shaped!!! →

Subject: Science

Favourite topic: Our solar system!

Quirks, ticks or odd behaviour: Can breathe without oxygen!!!

Any other information: Not 100% sure that she's 100% human!

Information supplied by:

Bernie Roberts class 5B

8

The heart of the Solar System

"Bernie Roberts! Get down off that desk!" shouted Miss Galaxy before she'd even got through the door to 5B.

Charming, I thought. There I was, preparing everyone for her lesson by doing my award-winning impersonation of the space shuttle, and I get told off! I climbed on to my chair and then on to the floor.

Miss Galaxy looked at me and smiled. She's not that bad, see? It's just that, in my official job as 5B's Class Joker I seem to get more tickings-off than the others. That's the price of fame, I suppose. Everyone in Pickle Hill knows Bernie Roberts.

"Right," said Miss Galaxy, waddling over to

the teacher's desk, "as promised, we're going to be spending my next few lessons taking a look at space –"

"The final frontier?" asked Emily Chickpea, with a grin.

"The space between Bernie's ears?" asked Dripping. How kind.

"Our galaxy, our solar system, stars, planets, moons, meteors, and much, much more!" said Miss Galaxy.

"Including black holes?" asked Noel the Know-All.

"Including black holes," Miss Galaxy nodded.

Before I go any further, I think I'd better explain a few things. For starters, Emily Chickpea's name isn't really Emily Chickpea, it's Emily Chigby. Dripping's name isn't really Dripping but David Ripping – D. Ripping – but Noel the Know-All even calls *himself* Noel the Know-All, so I'm not being horrible, right? Right. Good, so can I get on now, please? Thank you. Oh, just one more thing. It's about Miss Galaxy and the reason why she waddles. It's because she's planet-shaped, see? She's almost a perfect round whatchamacallit (sphere?). And being so round she waddles rather than walks. She's not big, mind you. Just planet-shaped.

"Bernie?" Miss Galaxy smiled. "I know we're about to take a tour around the solar system, but would you mind coming back down to Earth for a minute? You were miles away."

"Sorry, Miss," I said. She was right. "I was imagining unarmed combat with an alien creature: a green version of Mr Smudge the caretaker, but with more arms."

Just about everyone laughed.

"Do you think there is intelligent life on other planets?" asked Noel.

"Do you think there's intelligent life in Pickle Hill Primary?" I asked. I can't help it. I'm a laugh a minute, me!

"Wait and see," said Miss Galaxy, with her serious teacher face on. "Let's begin the tour."

She lifted the lid of her desk and out floated a basketball that drifted up into the air above her head and began to spin. As it spun, faster and faster, it turned into a ball of fire.

We gasped in amazement.

IMAGINE THIS IS THE SUN — OUR SUN — AT THE CENTRE OF OUR SOLAR SYSTEM. IT'S AN ENORMOUS BALL OF BLAZING GASES.

"What's a solar system, Miss Galaxy?" asked Dripping.

"A solar system is a star and all the planets and moons that orbit it. In our solar system, we have the Sun at the centre and the Earth and other planets spinning around it."

"The Sun is a star?" gasped Mary-Jane.

"Stars are suns?" gasped Dripping.

"Both right!" nodded Miss Galaxy.

To be honest, I was still a bit distracted by the flaming ball of gas spinning around above Miss Galaxy's head – after all, it's not something you see every day!

"So there are billions of stars out there which are also suns and which have solar systems all of their very own?" gasped Sunita.

Miss Galaxy nodded excitedly. "What's more, as far as stars go, our sun isn't a very big one! It's more medium-sized. In fact, it's only about a million times bigger than the Earth."

"A million times bigger!" gulped Sunita. "It doesn't look that big on charts."

"Because charts aren't drawn to scale," Miss Galaxy explained. "They simply show the position of the stars and planets, not their sizes or how far apart they really are."

"If they did, you'd need a mega-huge piece of paper!" I added, helpfully.

"Very true," beamed Miss Galaxy. She pointed up to our very own mini-sun, spinning above her head. "Now, the Sun is many things but, most of all, it's hot: H-O-T. Staggeringly so."

NEVER, EVER, EVER LOOK DIRECTLY AT THE SUN, EVEN WITH SUNGLASSES!

HOW MANY STARS ARE THERE?

WE'RE IN A GALAXY CALLED THE MILKY WAY, MADE UP OF ABOUT 100 BILLION STARS. THERE ARE PROBABLY BILLIONS OF OTHER GALAXIES IN SPACE.

Alice Smith stuck her hand up. She doesn't talk much, except in lessons about animals – then it's hard to shut her up. "Miss?" she said.

"Yes, Alice?"

"If the Sun's so hot, why doesn't it burn us all up?"

"Because we're so far away!" said Max Morrison, who must have just woken up.

"Ninety-three million miles may sound a long way from the Sun, Max," said Miss Galaxy, opening her desk lid again, "but it's not distance alone that protects us from the Sun's rays."

This time, a tennis ball floated out of her desk and began to orbit our miniature Sun and, as it did, it turned into a tiny Earth.

"That's down to the Earth's atmosphere," Miss Galaxy went on, and at the mention of the word "atmosphere" small clouds formed around parts of our tiny, tennis-ball Earth. "The air keeps out most, but not all, of the Sun's harmful rays … but, without the Sun, the Earth's temperature would drop to around *minus* 270°C!"

Suddenly, the miniature Sun fizzled out and became a basketball once again. The whole classroom became icy cold and everything frosted like the inside of a freezer! We all were sh-sh-shivering like crazy, and there was a chorus of chattering teeth and cries of "It's f-f-freezing!" Miss Galaxy even had icicles on the end of her nose!

WATER FREEZES AT 0°C, SO THINK HOW COLD −270°C MUST BE!!!

We were all beginning to wonder if we were going to end up frozen statues when the Sun flared back to life and the classroom warmed up again.

"Now I know what it's like to be a penguin," I said, but everyone seemed too busy rubbing their hands together or massaging the feeling back into their ears to find it funny.

"Hang on, Miss," said Emily, at last. "If stars are other suns, millions of miles away, how come they only come out at night?"

"An excellent question!" said Miss Galaxy, bouncing up and down a bit like an excited beach ball (if beach balls can get excited). "Can anyone answer it?"

Surprise, surprise, Noel the Know-All could. "The stars *are* shining all the time, it's just that we can't see them in the daytime because the light from our sun is brighter than them –"

"So they don't show up. An excellent answer, Noel. Stars don't come out at night. They're there all the time, twinkling away, but you just can't see them."

"Then why can't we see the Sun shining all the time?" I asked, which was fair enough.

"Because it shines on different parts of the Earth at different times, Bernie," said Miss Galaxy. "You see, the Earth is not only orbiting the Sun, it's also spinning around as it goes. It takes 24 hours for the Earth to take one full spin, which is why a single day and night is made up of 24 hours."

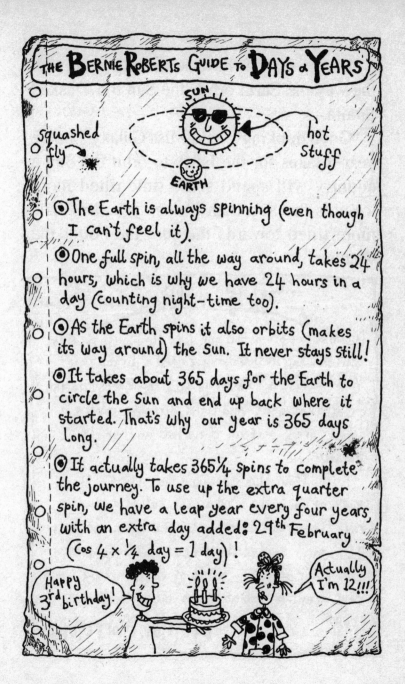

- The Earth is always spinning (even though I can't feel it).

- One full spin, all the way around, takes 24 hours, which is why we have 24 hours in a day (counting night-time too).

- As the Earth spins it also orbits (makes its way around) the Sun. It never stays still!

- It takes about 365 days for the Earth to circle the Sun and end up back where it started. That's why our year is 365 days long.

- It actually takes 365¼ spins to complete the journey. To use up the extra quarter spin, we have a leap year every four years, with an extra day added: 29th February (cos $4 \times \frac{1}{4}$ day = 1 day) !

"Do the seasons have something to do with the way the Earth orbits the Sun too?" asked Sunita.

"Good thinking!" said Miss Galaxy. "In the year it takes for the Earth to orbit the Sun a country will spend some time tilted more towards the Sun than it does at others. The more tilted towards the sun, the hotter the weather."

The Sun's Rays

When a ray from the Sun hits the Earth straight on it's what Miss Galaxy called a direct ray. And because a direct ray hits the Earth straight on, all that heat and light directly covers a small area making it as hot and bright as possible.

A ray from the Sun which hits the Earth at more of an angle is what she called a slanting ray. These rays cover a larger area. Because these rays spread their heat and light over this wider area, the parts of Earth hit by these rays aren't as hot as those hit with direct rays.

by Max Morrison

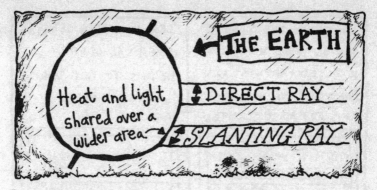

"As we all know, the seasons are spring, summer, autumn and winter," said Miss Galaxy, and, somehow, the seasons changed outside 5B's windows as she spoke!

SUMMER IS THE HOTTEST SEASON, WHEN A COUNTRY IS TILTED MOST DIRECTLY TOWARDS THE SUN.

AUTUMN IS WHEN A COUNTRY BEGINS TO TILT AWAY FROM THE SUN AND THE RAYS ARE MORE SLANTED AND LESS STRONG.

WINTER IS THE COLDEST SEASON, WHEN THE COUNTRY IS TILTED FARTHEST AWAY FROM THE SUN AND THE RAYS ARE MOST SLANTED.	SPRING IS THE SEASON WHEN THE COUNTRY BEGINS TO TILT MORE TOWARDS THE SUN AGAIN.

"Wow!" said Mary-Jane. "That was like a whole year's weather in under a minute!"

"But it doesn't explain why some places are sunny all the time ... I mean, in some countries isn't it like summer all year round?" asked Max.

"And what about the North Pole?" I asked. "I'll bet not many people choose to spend their summer holidays there!"

Miss Galaxy picked up her handbag, opened it and pulled out a globe which I guarantee you couldn't possibly have fitted there in the first place. If it had, the bag would have looked like a snake that had swallowed a whole Christmas pudding. Well, that's Pickle Hill Primary for you, I suppose.

"When the Earth is spinning as it also orbits the Sun, it doesn't spin absolutely upright. It spins as though there's a straight rod going through it at an angle. This is called the Earth's axis. The Earth spins on a tilt, and that means that some places are always tilted more directly towards the sun than others," she explained.

THIS ROD THIS GLOBE SPINS ON REPRESENTS THE EARTH'S AXIS.

"And the parts of the Earth that tilt most directly towards the Sun have the hottest summers!" said – no prizes for guessing – Noel the Know-All.

"Spot on, Noel! The place on Earth that is tilted most directly towards the Sun all the time is the equator. That's actually an imaginary line running crossways around the middle of the Earth. It's used to divide the Earth into the northern and southern hemispheres … with north at the top, south at the bottom."

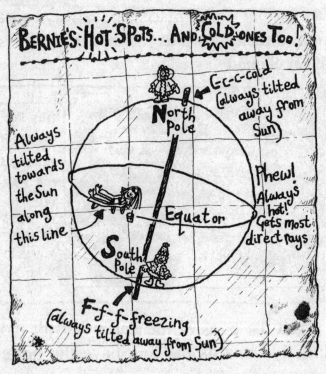

BERNIE'S HOT SPOTS… AND COLD ONES TOO!

G-c-c-cold (always tilted away from Sun)

North Pole

Always tilted towards the Sun along this line

Phew! Always hot! Gets most direct rays

Equator

South Pole

F-f-f-freezing (always tilted away from Sun)

Suddenly, Dave Horris stuck up his hand – which, let me tell you, is about as usual as an elephant laying an egg (unless the topic is football).

"Yes, David?" said Miss Galaxy, trying not to look surprised.

"Didn't you say stars were suns too, Miss?" he asked, slowly.

"Yes," nodded our teacher. "A while ago…"

"Then why do stars twinkle but the Sun doesn't?" asked Dave.

Miss Galaxy beamed. "I must say, 5B, you really have been asking me some excellent questions. I'll answer that next lesson, when we look at the other planets in our solar system."

A moment later, the bell rang.

Meet the planets!

Our next lesson with Miss Galaxy was after lunch the following day. Dripping had eaten too many chips and kept groaning and clutching his stomach and Mary-Jane had a big, orange baked-bean stain on her shirt!

When we walked – or rather ran – into our classroom, Miss Galaxy was already there and had drawn a diagram on the blackboard.

"Good afternoon, 5B!" she said. "Here on

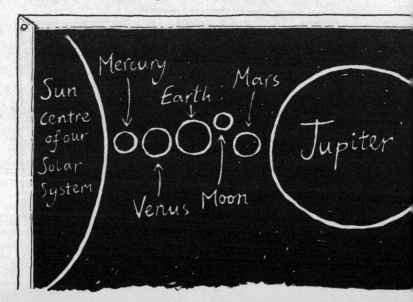

Sun
Centre
of our
Solar
System

Mercury

Earth

Mars

Venus

Moon

Jupiter

the board are the nine planets in our solar system. The Solar System is everything that moves around the Sun. Other stars – other suns – have their own solar systems, with their own planets moving around them."

Sunita stuck her hand up. "You've drawn ten planets on the board, Miss. Not nine."

"No she hasn't," said Noel the Know-All, looking so excited that he knew better! "The Moon isn't a planet!"

"What is it, then?" asked Sunita.

"It's a moon!" said Noel.

"Noel's right," said Miss Galaxy. "Planets only orbit the Sun. Moons orbit planets…"

"…which orbit the Sun!" I added. I was getting the hang of this space business.

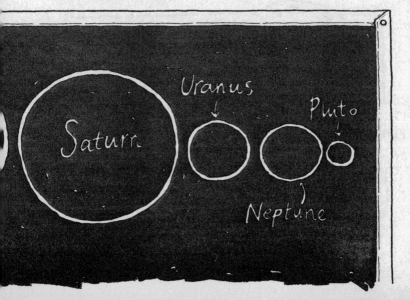

"Exactly, Bernie. In fact, most of the planets have their own moons too. The Solar System is made up of the nine planets, their 70 or so moons, and asteroids and comets, all of which move around the Sun … but I've only shown our moon – which we usually just refer to as *the* Moon – on the board."

"What's the difference between an asteroid and a comet?" asked Max Morrison.

"I'll show you," said Miss Galaxy. "Open the bottom of the middle window please, Mandy."

Little Mandy Patterson just managed it. A moment later, without a sound, a huge rock – bigger than an armchair – came spinning through the doorway. That was weird enough but, weirder still, it seemed to be moving in slow motion.

Surely nothing that big and that heavy could move through the sky so slowly without falling?

"This hunk of rock is an asteroid," said Miss Galaxy. "A very small one." It sailed past Mandy and out of the bottom of the window. At the same time, a great big ball of something else came spinning slowly through the door. "This one's a comet," said Miss Galaxy, excitedly. "Unlike the asteroid, most of it is made up of ice." That disappeared through the window too.

"Now, there are three important things I want you to remember," said Miss Galaxy. "Firstly, some of the planets in the Solar System are made of rock, like the Earth, and some are made of liquids and gases. Secondly, my drawing on the blackboard isn't to scale – the planets are really millions of miles apart. And, thirdly, the space between the planets isn't air but space!"

There were a few puzzled frowns around the classroom.

"So what exactly is space, Miss?" someone asked. It might even have been me!

At that moment, there was a knock at the window and we all turned to see something floating outside 5B, tapping at the glass. It seemed to have a huge head and one giant eye. Then I realized what it was! I laughed, dashed across the room and pulled the window up, and an *astronaut* came floating in.

HI, EVERYONE! IT SURE IS GREAT TO BE HERE. CONDITIONS ARE GOOD.

"The children were wondering what space is made up of," said Miss Galaxy, who'd obviously been expecting our guest!

"Well, kids," said the astronaut, who was slowly spinning across the classroom above our heads. "Earth has an atmosphere: the gases which give us fluffy clouds, beautiful blue skies and the all-important air which we breathe." He bumped into a strip light, but carried on moving slowly above us. "There ain't no air in space, though. It's a vacuum. It's nothingness. If you threw a ball in space, it'd keep on going. There'd be no wind to slow it down. No air resistance. There's no sound, either, which was why that there comet and asteroid you just saw were so slow and so silent when they came through here. Without air to carry sound, there's silence."

"That's why you're wearing a space helmet and oxygen tanks, isn't it?" asked Noel the Know-All. "Because you can't breathe in space."

"Smart kid!" said the astronaut. "I have my own oxygen supply in this here space suit. Without it, I couldn't breathe and I'd die."

Dripping hurried over to the door and opened it in time for the astronaut to float out the way that the asteroid and comet had come floating in.

"See you guys on the Moon!" he shouted, as he drifted away.

"Did he just say that he'd see us on the Moon?" I gawped.

Miss Galaxy looked at me while trying not to smile. "Oh, sorry, didn't I mention that? We'll be going to the Moon next lesson."

"COOL!" said Dripping.

"Are we *really* going, Miss?" asked Alice. Miss Galaxy had sounded so casual about the trip to the Moon, as if she was just talking about a trip down the shops to buy a packet of frozen peas!

"Of course we're going," she said. "In the meantime, can anyone remember the question we ended on last lesson?"

Guess who stuck their hand up. Go on. Guess, guess, guess. Wrong, wrong, wrong! It wasn't Noel the Know-All but Dave Horris. "I asked why stars twinkled and the Sun didn't," he said.

"And now I'll tell you why," said Miss Galaxy. "It has to do with the Earth's atmosphere again." She drew a diagram, and we copied it down.

"Because the air in the atmosphere is moving and changing it sometimes makes the starlight look brighter and sometimes dimmer, and that's why stars look as though they're twinkling. The Sun is so big and so bright and so close to Earth that it can shine through its atmosphere without being distorted at all."

LIGHT IN SPACE

by Sunita

Light-year ruler!

* The only body to give off light in our solar system is the Sun.

* The shining of the Moon is really light reflected from the Sun.

* The distance of planets from Earth is measured in "light-years". That's the number of years it takes for the light from a star to reach Earth. Light travels about 9.5 million million km (or 6 million million miles) in a year.

* After the Sun, the nearest star is Proxima Centauri. It's about four light-years away.

* This means that the light of Proxima Centauri which we can see in the sky today actually left the star four years ago.

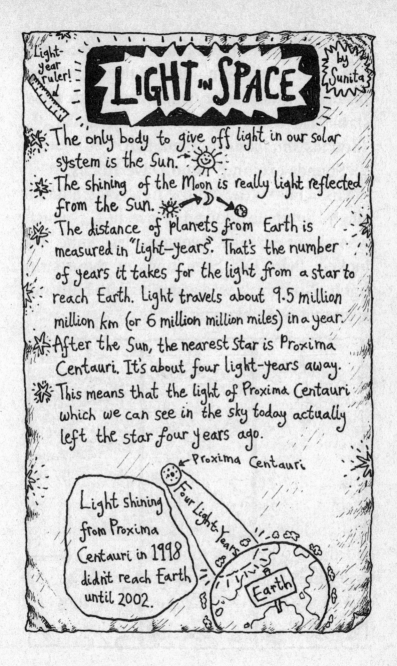

Proxima Centauri

Four Light Years

Earth

Light shining from Proxima Centauri in 1998 didn't reach Earth until 2002.

"Now, the thing about most stars – and that includes the Sun – is that they don't last for ever," Miss Galaxy continued, with a sad sigh. "The really big ones go supernova…"

"Sounds *sooooooper!*" I laughed.

"Sounds exciting!" said Dave Horris.

Miss Galaxy flicked the light switch and a single lightbulb glowed above us … which was a bit strange because, last time I'd looked, there had been rows of those strip lights. Now there was a single, bare bulb and even that was changing…

"Supernovas are when suns actually explode and die," Miss Galaxy told us, "Ours won't do that but it will swell up, become 10,000 brighter, and is likely to destroy the Earth."

There were gasps of horror.

"Don't panic!" said Miss Galaxy. "That won't happen for another 5,000,000,000 years!"

Then Noel suddenly got all excited and bounced up and down in his chair, with his hand up.

MISS, IF A STAR BLOWS UP TEN LIGHT-YEARS AWAY, IT'LL TAKE TEN YEARS FOR US TO FIND OUT!

WOW! THAT MEANS WE COULD BE LOOKING AT THE LIGHT OF A STAR THAT ISN'T EVEN THERE ANY MORE!

"And I think that amazing thought is a good place to end today's lesson," said Miss Galaxy. "Next lesson, we'll walk on the Moon!"

The whole class cheered.

One small step for a man...

The moment Miss Galaxy came into our classroom for our next lesson, and shut the door behind her, something very strange happened. I felt so much lighter! The next minute, me and the rest of 5B were floating in mid-air...

But not just us. Our desks were too, along with everything that had been on them: pencils, rulers, rubbers, Alice's lucky troll…

"The thing which usually keeps our feet firmly on the ground is an invisible force called gravity," Miss Galaxy explained, as she drifted past me, looking even more like a planet than ever before! "It's Earth's gravity which pulls a ball back down when you throw it up in the air. If there wasn't any gravity, the ball would go up into space… In fact, there wouldn't be any air, because it's the Earth's gravity that holds our atmosphere in place too."

IN A SPACECRAFT THE FORCE OF GRAVITY FROM THE EARTH OR MOON ISN'T STRONG ENOUGH TO PULL THE ASTRONAUTS DOWN!

Dave Horris, who was floating past me, rolled himself up into a ball and rocked himself forward. He went spinning across the classroom in roll after roll of slow-motioning somersaults!

THIS IS BRILLIANT!!

"Imagine what it must be like for astronauts trying to fly a rocket while they're floating about like this!" laughed Max, drifting past our teacher.

"Good point, Max," beamed Miss Galaxy. "Astronauts have to eat, drink and sleep whilst floating around, though they spend some of their time strapped into chairs. That's why they have weightlessness training before going into space."

WHAT'S THAT FLOATING BLOB?

ORANGE JUICE. WITHOUT GRAVITY LIQUIDS FLOAT TOO!

We all had a great time. I found I could float over to one wall, twist myself around and push off from the wall with my feet – like you do in a swimming pool – and send myself off in the opposite direction.

Emily Chickpea did some very girlie ballet-type spins above the desks which, I have to admit, looked great. It was wicked!

"Time to come down now, 5B," grinned Miss Galaxy, who'd been quietly spinning in mid-air in her planet-like way!

On the word "down", we all floated slowly back down to the ground, which was a real shame. That had been *brilliant fun* and we all – well, most of us, anyway – wished that we could have stayed up there even longer.

There was a bit of sorting out to do before we were all back at our desks, with a few arguments between the girls over whose furry pencil case was whose.

"Of course, the Pickle Hill way of getting to the Moon will be somewhat different to the normal method," Miss Galaxy grinned. "So let's look at the rocket that took the first people there."

And there on the board was a diagram that I could have sworn – but it's rude to swear! – hadn't been there a milli-second before. It showed something called the *Saturn V* rocket. We copied it down.

DRIPPINGS ROCKET
(No, not a big firework!!!)

SPACECRAFT bit with astronauts in it.

One super-ginormous FUEL TANK.

BLASTERS to blast the whole thing free from Earth's gravity.

One of the trickiest parts of flying to the Moon is breaking free of Earth's gravity, which is pulling the spacecraft down, like an invisible giant hand.

A **VERY, VERY, VERY** big rocket is needed to blast the spacecraft fast enough and high enough to get it far enough away from this powerful pull.

The actual spacecraft part of a rocket, with people inside, is only a small part at the top: the nose cone.

The rest of the rocket is full of the HUGE amount of fuel needed to power the rocket and the blasters which are needed to get the whole thing up in space!

FUEL   FUEL   MORE FUEL   FUEL

"The first human to set foot on the Moon was American astronaut Neil Armstrong," Miss Galaxy told us. "He was one of three astronauts on the *Apollo 11* mission in July 1969. Their *Saturn* rocket came in a number of sections, with many parts ejected soon after take-off."

She opened the top of the teacher's desk, leaving the lid upright, and it turned into a television screen!

WHEN THE TIME WAS RIGHT...

THE TWO REMAINING PARTS OF THE ROCKET SEPARATED.

WHILE MICHAEL COLLINS PILOTED THE CAPSULE AROUND THE MOON...

THE LUNAR MODULE, CALLED THE EAGLE, HEADED FOR THE SURFACE.

INSIDE WERE NEIL ARMSTRONG AND BUZZ ALDRIN.

THEY LANDED JUST AS THEIR FUEL RAN OUT!

THE EAGLE HAS LANDED!

AS NEIL ARMSTRONG STEPPED OFF THE BOTTOM RUNG OF THE LADDER AND BECAME THE FIRST HUMAN BEING TO SET FOOT ON THE MOON, HE SAID:

"What Armstrong meant to say was 'One small step for *a* man…' but, in all the excitement, he fluffed his lines, and who can blame him!"

"He wasn't the first person in space, though, was he?" said Dripping.

"No," said Miss Galaxy. "That honour goes to the Russian Yuri Gagarin and the first space flight on 12th April 1961."

"But when are *we* going?" whined Alice.

Miss Galaxy glanced at the clock. "Well, I'm sorry, 5B. What with all that floating we did, I'm afraid we've run out of time. We'll have to go to the Moon in our next lesson!"

Destination Moon

"To avoid disappointment, our trip to the Moon will begin shortly," said Miss Galaxy, waddling into our classroom for her next lesson, "but there are a few things you need to know about the place before we go."

"How long will it take us to get there?" asked Alice. "Only, I promised to go round to Gemma's house later and feed her guinea pig…"

"At the moment, it takes about three days to reach the Moon," said Miss Galaxy. "The first mission to the Moon took just eight days there and back, with plenty of time for sightseeing in between. But, as I said earlier, the Pickle Hill Primary method of space travel is a bit different. It'll have us back in plenty of time for feeding animals!"

We cheered.

Miss Galaxy drew a perfect circle on the

board in one go. A moment later, it glowed with a silvery light.

"Unlike the Earth, the Moon doesn't have any atmosphere," Miss Galaxy began.

"What, none at all?" asked Dripping.

"Zero, zilch, nought," she nodded.

"Is that because the Moon's gravity isn't strong enough to hold an atmosphere in place?" asked the walking-talking-brain-box Noel the Know-All.

"Excellent!" said Miss Galaxy, her eyes lighting up. "If you look closely, you'll see that there are big dark, flat patches on the Moon. We call them seas, but there isn't any water in them. There are also lots and lots of dark rings. These are craters. They were made when rocks crashed on to the surface."

"Don't forget that, although the Moon seems to shine brightly sometimes, it's really the light of the Sun reflected on the Moon."

"The Sun is shining on half of the Moon all of the time, it's just that we can't always see that from Earth." She pointed at the glowing image of the Moon on the blackboard and, as she spoke, it changed.

"The Moon is never really changing shape, it's just that our view of it from Earth is different," said Miss Galaxy. "However, because of the way both the Earth and the Moon spin, there is one side of the Moon that we can never see from Earth. We call that 'the far side of the Moon'."

"No prizes for guessing why," I grinned.

"On very rare occasions, the Moon can block out sunlight, though!" Miss Galaxy went on. "This is called an eclipse of the Sun. Here, I'll show you."

Suddenly, she had a grapefruit in her hand. Don't ask me where it came from, but I'll bet you all the greengrocers in Britain that it hadn't been there a moment before. She threw it up in the air and it stopped dead and started burning and fizzing like our real Sun.

Next, she threw a small apple – yes, *apple*! – up in the air, about the size of a snooker ball.

48

Just then, the small apple Moon passed right in front of my eyes, perfectly blocking out the grapefruit Sun behind.

"You can still see the glow from the Sun around the edge of the Moon," said our teacher. "That's called the corona."

Quite suddenly, the grapefruit became a grapefruit again and fell into Miss Galaxy's hand. The small apple fell into the other. She juggled them absent-mindedly. "It takes about 28 days for the Moon to orbit the Earth," she said, "meanwhile, the Earth itself is taking 365¼ days to orbit the Sun."

"What about the planets, Miss? Do they all take 365¼ days to orbit the Sun, like the Earth does?" asked Emily Chickpea.

"No. Remember the diagram you copied from the board? Well, the further away a planet is from the Sun, the longer it takes to complete an orbit. Pluto is the farthest away and takes 248 years!"

"So, if one Earth year is one Earth orbit, then one Pluto year is 248 Earth years!" said Max.

"Which means everyone on Pluto will have died of old age long before their first birthday!"

I laughed. I do tell some excellent gags!

"Enough tittle-tattle," said Miss Galaxy. "It's time for you all to strap yourselves in."

Suddenly, we found our desks and chairs swivelling to face the windows, with us in them. There was a loud CLUNK and not only was all the furniture now bolted to the floor, but lights and buttons flashed on our desks. They'd become control panels! And the windows had become one big one, showing nothing outside but blue sky and a fluffy cloud or two. This was *brilliant*!

"Ten, nine, eight, seven, six, five, four, three, two, one! Ignition. We have blast off!" said a voice, and I felt myself being pushed back into my chair by some invisible force. I managed to turn and look at the others, and their faces looked all wobbly as we – the whole classroom! – launched into space.

Outside the window, we passed through cloud at incredible speed and then, suddenly, as we left the Earth's atmosphere, everything went from blue to black. We were in space! The feeling of being pressed down on stopped. I unbuckled my seatbelt and floated over to the window.

There, far below us – where the playground used to be! – was Earth, hanging in space.

"Bernie Roberts!" snapped Miss Galaxy. "If you don't strap yourself in, you'll bump your head. We're coming in to land."

She needn't have told us. There was quite a BUMP! (And on my head too, because I got back to my seat too late! My fault, of course … but just one of the risks you have to take as official class joker.)

"Everyone into their space suits!" Miss Galaxy ordered. "There's a moon to explore!"

With a cheer, there was a mid-air scramble as everyone unbuckled themselves and "swam" through the air – like we did in our practice – to the space suits and tried to pull them on. Imagine trying to get dressed as you're floating, weightless, around your bedroom… Now imagine, instead of putting on ordinary clothes, trying to put on a space suit with heavy boots and a goldfish-bowl helmet! That's why it seemed to take ages before everyone was ready.

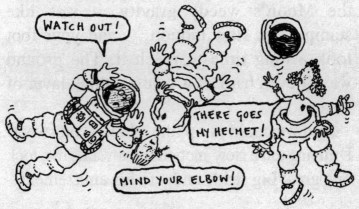

One giant leap for 5B

The first thing I noticed when I stepped out on to the Moon was how quiet everything was, and it wasn't just because of the big space helmets we were wearing. They had built-in speakers so we could hear everything around us. It's just that there was nothing to hear, and no wind – no air – to carry it, anyway!

Even our footsteps were silent, despite our clumping-great boots! You couldn't stamp your foot hard on the ground because, with the Moon's weedy gravity, it was like stamping in slow motion … and your foot took a long time to reach it. The ground wasn't even hard. It was just a thick layer of dusty soil.

And we could jump like athletes, no sweat! Dripping did a slow-motion run towards me, took one great big stride and – to his amazement –

found himself doing a super-ginormous leap right up into the air. Only it wasn't really "air", of course. It was nothingness. It was *space*!

Now we all had a go, and were leaping up off the Moon's surface with the greatest of *eeeeeeease*! Mandy Patterson is so small and light that I reckon, if she'd taken her space boots off, she'd have floated off in space, never to be seen again – which would have been a terrible thing, because she still owes me 50p from the other week!

"Gather round!" Miss Galaxy ordered. "That's enough of the Olympic Moon-Jumping Event for the time being." We laughed.

It was quite difficult to tell who was who with all of us wearing astronauts' suits that looked just the same, with oxygen tanks strapped to the back. There was no problem spotting Miss G, though. Not because her suit was planet-shaped, but because she wasn't wearing one!!! (Yes, that was three exclamation marks.) She stood there, on the surface of the Moon, the same way that she stood at the front of the class. She didn't seem to need air to breathe!

"The Moon's gravity may not seem very strong as you leap about here, but it's strong enough to affect the Earth's seas and oceans," she explained. "You see, it's the pull of the Moon's gravity that creates the tides – the sea going in and out on a beach – back home. As the Moon orbits Earth, it pulls on different seas and oceans at different times, making all the different tides."

WOW! IT'S PRETTY COOL THAT A DUST-BOWL BALL OF A PLACE LIKE THIS HAS SUCH POWER!

Miss Galaxy nodded. "Twice a month, when there's a full or new Moon, the Moon and the Sun are lined up with each other, and their combined gravity – joint pull – on the Earth's oceans create the highest tides of the year," said Miss Galaxy, walking off to her left. We followed.

We walked around the side of a crater and there, parked in front of us, was some kind of car! We all gathered around it.

"Remember the astronaut we met earlier? Well, he and his buddies left many things behind after their visits here," said Miss Galaxy. "Mainly because there was no way they could take them home. They needed the lunar module they took off in to be as light as possible. They planted flags, of course, and Apollo 15 left a small memorial to the 14 American astronauts and Russian cosmonauts who died over the years in the race to explore space. But most things were left behind because they had to be."

By now, Dave Horris had climbed into the Lunar Rover's driving seat.

"Can I give it a go, M-iss!" he asked, and on the word "Miss" the vehicle lurched forward, with Dave in it, and he was off. We all cheered!

After that, all of us who wanted a go took turns at driving the Lunar Rover.

"Didn't that astronaut we met in the classroom say he'd see us on the Moon?" Mary-Jane asked Miss Galaxy. Suddenly, I heard the noise of a man clearing his throat behind me, and, sure enough, there he was!

WHAT'S GOING ON HERE THEN?

"When you guys have quite finished playing with my Lunar Rover, I'll have it back now ... if that's OK with you?" said the astronaut. He sounded stern. Dripping brought the moon car to a halt and climbed out. "Thanks," said the astronaut. "This ain't no toy," he went on. "This baby is one piece of high-tech equipment."

"Or *was*," Miss Galaxy whispered to us. "Computer technology has changed beyond recognition since the last Moon landings."

The astronaut obviously caught what she'd said, and didn't like what he heard. He looked really grumpy, inside that goldfish-bowl helmet. (Or "*real* grumpy", as he'd have put it, in that American drawl of his!)

He showed us a camera mounted on the front of the Rover. "This is the neat little gizmo that took live TV pictures of the lunar module taking off from the Moon's surface," he explained.

As official class joker – even on the Moon – I stepped in front of the lens, grinned and said "CHEESE!"

Did I imagine it, or did the inside of his helmet steam up a little? He didn't say anything to me, though, and carried on talking about the TV pictures.

REAL HARD TO BELIEVE, I KNOW, KIDS, BUT THIS TINY TRANSMITTING SATELLITE DISH BEAMED THE PICTURES TO RECEIVING DISHES BACK ON EARTH.

ACTUALLY, NOWADAYS IT'S NO BIG DEAL... LOTS OF PEOPLE HAVE SATELLITE DISH RECEIVERS ON THE SIDE OF THEIR HOUSES!

Before we knew it, 5B's trip to the Moon was over. It was time to head for home… well, back to Pickle Hill, at least! We said goodbye to the astronaut and piled back into our classroom spaceship, took off our space suits, strapped ourselves into our desks and – *five, four, three, two, one* – we blasted off and headed for home.

Because the Moon's gravity is so weedy, we didn't need much of a blast to break us free of its pull and to launch us back into space.

It was next-to-no-time before the view outside the windows was the Pickle Hill playground and beyond. We were home.

"Did we really just go to the Moon and back?" asked Alice.

"Well, you certainly didn't imagine it, if that's what you mean," said Max.

But I know what Alice meant. You're never quite sure what is and *isn't* at Pickle Hill Primary! And things certainly hadn't been so easy for the astronauts who'd gone before us!

The bell rang for the end of the lesson.

"See you all again tomorrow!" said Miss Galaxy.

Meet Mercury, Venus and Mars

"The planet nearest the Sun is Mercury," said Miss Galaxy as she bounced into our classroom at the start of her next lesson with us.

"And is made of old thermometers," I said, getting in my first joke good and quick. No one laughed! Sometimes I think I'm wasted on this audience.

"Both the liquid metal mercury in thermometers and the planet Mercury are named after the same character: Mercury, the Roman god," she continued, without batting an eyelid. "In fact, all of the planets in our solar system are named after manly Roman gods – Mars, Jupiter, Saturn, Uranus, Neptune, Pluto – except for two. Can you name them?"

Noel had his hand up first, but Miss Galaxy asked Sunita.

"The Earth and – er – Venus," said Sunita.

"Correct!" said Miss Galaxy. "Venus is named after a *she* – a goddess, not a god."

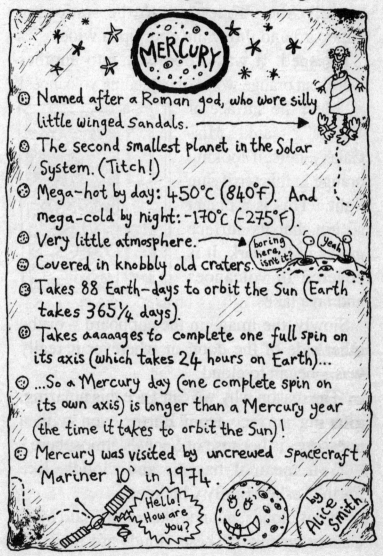

MERCURY

- Named after a Roman god, who wore silly little winged sandals.
- The second smallest planet in the Solar System. (Titch!)
- Mega-hot by day: 450°C (840°F). And mega-cold by night: -170°C (-275°F).
- Very little atmosphere.
- Covered in knobbly old craters.
- Takes 88 Earth-days to orbit the Sun (Earth takes 365¼ days).
- Takes aaaaages to complete one full spin on its axis (which takes 24 hours on Earth)...
- ...So a Mercury day (one complete spin on its own axis) is longer than a Mercury year (the time it takes to orbit the Sun)!
- Mercury was visited by uncrewed spacecraft 'Mariner 10' in 1974.

boring here, isn't it? / Yeah

Hello! How are you?

by Alice Smith

"After Mercury comes Venus," Miss Galaxy announced. "Now, stay at your desks. Nobody move!" She strode over to the stationery cupboard and threw the door open wide.

I gasped. It was a doorway into another world: an orange world of exploding volcanoes!

"Meet the surface of Venus!" said Miss Galaxy, herself looking orange in this terrifying light. "This is a planet so hot that its surface glows in the dark. It is covered in volcanoes and lava lakes…"

Slowly, the image in the cupboard – or the other side of the door, or wherever it really was – began to cloud.

"The reason why we can't see this amazing, glowing surface from Earth, even with a telescope, is because of Venus's atmosphere."

"You mean it has air and clouds, like Earth?" asked Emily Chickpea.

"It has clouds, but not like Earth," said Miss Galaxy, grimly. "These clouds are made of acid. Instead of air, there's deadly carbon dioxide gas. The pressure of this gas is not only so strong that it'd crush a human, it also traps the heat of the Sun."

SO, ON VENUS, YOU'D EITHER GET BURNT TO A FRAZZLE BY THE HEAT OR THE ACID, CRUSHED BY THE PRESSURE, OR SUFFOCATED?

GREAT CHOICES!

GREAT FOR HOLIDAYS!

"After Mercury and Venus comes Earth and then the fourth planet from the Sun, Mars … and no chocolate jokes, please," said Miss Galaxy, staring straight at me, for some strange reason, while keeping a straight face. As if I would! I just grinned.

"Because Mars is red in colour and named after the mighty Roman god of war, you'd probably expect it to be bigger and hotter than Earth. In fact, it's smaller and colder. Colder, because it's further away from the Sun. It does have a very impressive volcano on it, though. It's three times higher than Mount Everest!"

"Not that anyone would be mad enough to climb it!" I added.

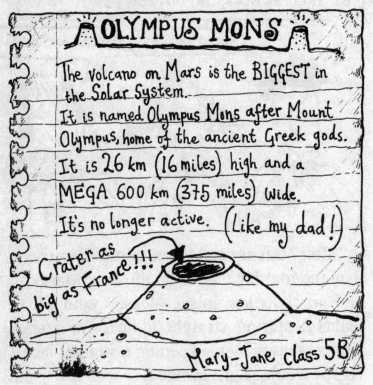

"What Mars used to be most famous for was its canals," said Miss Galaxy.

"Canals?" said Dripping. "You mean like the canals barges travel down?"

"Yes and no," said Miss Galaxy, which wasn't very helpful. "In the 19th century, some astronomers thought they could see canals on Mars."

"They must have had brilliant eyesight!" laughed Max, trying to do my job.

"Or very strong specs," I added, easily topping his weedy joke.

"They used telescopes, stupid!" said Noel.

"Exactly," nodded Miss Galaxy, waddling around to the front of her desk. "And, through their telescopes, they saw what appeared to be human-made canals... Look!"

She pointed above the blackboard and there, on the wall, was an image of the surface of a spooky red planet, as though we were looking through a telescope, with these very straight lines on it. They certainly looked as though someone had dug them.

"Only it couldn't be *humans* who'd made them," Miss Galaxy pointed out, "so the 19th-century astronomers decided that these canals were the work of Martians."

"But Martians are just pretend, Miss," said Alice, sounding less than sure. Tee! Hee!

"We know that now," said Miss Galaxy, "but we didn't know that back then."

"So what did these so-called canals turn out to be?" asked Mary-Jane.

"An optical illusion. A trick of the eye. The image on the wall is what it looks like looking at the surface of Mars through a telescope, through our own atmosphere. Everything's a bit blurred. Look at Mars from space, and it's a different matter." Miss Galaxy clicked her finger. Suddenly, the image became much sharper and what had looked like straight lines were now a load of unconnected dots – craters and things, I suppose. "The astronomers were simply joining up the dots in their mind!"

"But there might be life on other planets, mighten there, Miss?" said Alice, probably hoping the aliens looked like the horses she loved so much.

"Yes," nodded Miss Galaxy. "It's not impossible, as we'll see."

"WOW!" said a whole bunch of us.

"Has anyone – any human – ever been to Mars?" asked Tommy the Snooze from the very back of the class. I doubt I've mentioned him before because he spends most lessons asleep and very rarely moves – unless we're on a trip to the Moon – let alone asks a question!

"No human has ever been to Mars, but two human-made *Viking* probes have," said Miss Galaxy. "And, if we hurry to the playground, we may just be in time to see one."

We were out of that classroom and out of the building before you could say, "We have touchdown." We looked up in the air, expectantly.

It hit the grass with quite a thud. "The landing on Mars would have been much softer, with its lighter gravity," Miss Galaxy pointed out, as we rushed forward to study the space probe.

Miss Galaxy nipped around the machine, pointing out what bits did what so quickly that there appeared to be more than one of her! She was more excited than Dripping in a cake shop!

The *Viking* lander clicked and whirred as Miss Galaxy continued. "This machine contained so many different types of sensor that it could pretty much touch, taste and even smell Mars, and send the information back here… They didn't find a trace of life, but they did discover dried-up valleys caused by water wearing away the rock over the years …which is incredible because it means that Mars might once have supported life."

"But a moment ago you said that Martians were just pretend!" I protested.

"If they did once exist, they were more likely to have been single-cell organisms living in ponds. Not multi-celled walking, talking creatures like us," said Miss Galaxy. "They could have been rather like the amoeba here on Earth."

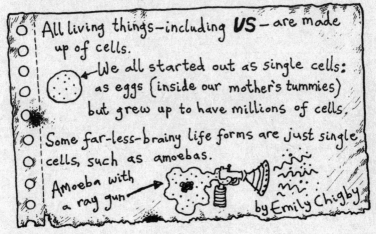

All living things—including **US**—are made up of cells.

We all started out as single cells: as eggs (inside our mother's tummies) but grew up to have millions of cells.

Some far-less-brainy life forms are just single cells, such as amoebas.

Amoeba with a ray gun →

by Emily Chigby

"Some scientists don't believe that there was even the most basic life form on Mars, let alone green monsters! We just don't know… Now, back to class everyone. The *Viking* probe has work to do!"

By Jupiter!

The next lesson with Miss Galaxy was first thing Monday morning, and she was in the classroom waiting for us as we piled in.

She had a big grin on her face, as though she was trying to hide some guilty secret. It's the sort of grin I have when I'm waiting for someone to discover the rubber rat in their pencil case!

We went to sit at our desks and fell straight through our chairs to the floor!

WHAT'S HAPPENING?

AM I A GHOST?

LOOKS SOLID ENOUGH!

Miss Galaxy chuckled, her whole round body wobbling with laughter. "I know that was a bit mean of me, but I wanted to remind you that just because something looks solid, doesn't mean that it is! Everyone up!" We stood up. "Right, now your chairs should be solid enough to sit in again."

We all sat down again … rather nervously!

"Now, 5B, the next planet in our tour of the Solar System – the fifth from the Sun – is Jupiter and it isn't like any of the planets we've encountered so far. It may look the familiar ball-shape, but it isn't solid at all. It's mainly a mixture of liquid hydrogen and liquid helium – so you couldn't stand on it."

HELIUM BALLOONS ARE THE ONES THAT FLOAT UP TO THE CEILING, AREN'T THEY?

YES, BECAUSE HELIUM IS LIGHTER THAN AIR.

"Jupiter is by far the biggest planet in our solar system. In fact – hold on to your hats – it's so very big that you could easily fit all the other eight planets inside it…"

"That's BIG," Dave Norris agreed, and there were a few other whistles and "coo"s of amazement around the class.

"It also spins faster than any of the other planets in the Solar System, so much so that it has what looks like a bulging waistline!" said our planet-shaped teacher. I looked at her tummy, but didn't dare say anything!

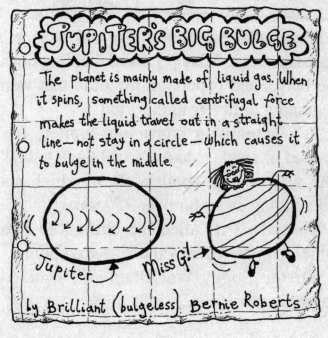

JUPITER'S BIG BULGE

The planet is mainly made of liquid gas. When it spins, something called centrifugal force makes the liquid travel out in a straight line — not stay in a circle — which causes it to bulge in the middle.

Jupiter

Miss G!

by Brilliant (bulgeless) Bernie Roberts

"Even if you could somehow stand on Jupiter's non-solid surface, you'd need more than a good pair of wellingtons and an umbrella," said Miss Galaxy, her voice rising above the sound of a wind – wind *inside* a classroom? – whipping up out of nowhere.

THE WEATHER ON JUPITER IS TERRIBLE. THE SPOTS YOU CAN SEE ON THE "SURFACE" ARE REALLY STORMS... HAS ANYONE HEARD OF THE GREAT RED SPOT?

Wasn't that the one on the end of Noel's nose last week, Miss?" I asked, holding down the books and papers on my desk that were beginning to flutter in the wind.

"It's actually a storm on Jupiter, first spotted in 1644 … and it's still there today!" She was talking about a storm which had been raging away for over *350 years*!

"But why's it called the Great Red Spot rather than the Great Cloud?" asked Sunita.

"Or the Soggy Wet Blanket?" I added, helpfully.

"Because that's what it looks like from Earth. A great red spot. It's so big, you can sometimes even see it through an ordinary telescope!" said Miss Galaxy.

"Is it true you can see Jupiter's moons through an ordinary pair of binoculars?" asked Max, shouting above the wind.

"Only four of them," said Miss Galaxy, hanging on to the edge of the teacher's desk, her hair blowing out behind her.

"*Four*?" I gasped. "How many does it have altogether, Miss?"

"Over 30!"

"That's plain greedy."

"Sorry?"

"THAT'S PLAIN GREE –"

I didn't get to finish my sentence because I was distracted by my desk blowing away and Mandy blowing past me!

WOODAAAAHHH!

WOOOSH!

We all ended up against the blackboard wall in a pile of chairs, desks, books and anything else that wasn't nailed down. Then, suddenly, the wind stopped.

First we'd fallen through non-solid chairs, and now we'd been blown to bits!

"An excellent way of remembering what conditions are like on Jupiter!" said Miss Galaxy with that guilty grin of hers back again!

"And from a liquid gas planet with terrible winds, we move to another one, more famous for its rings," said Miss Galaxy. "Any idea which one that may be?"

You didn't need to be Noel the Know-All to answer that one. The whole of 5B called out the answer together, in one big shout: SATURN!

Saturn and beyond

"Like Jupiter, Saturn is mainly made up of hydrogen and helium and is huge – second in size only to Jupiter," Miss Galaxy told us.

"Does it have loads of moons too, or is it quite happy with just the one like we are?" I asked.

"Actually, Bernie, we know it has at least 18 moons! Maybe more. Admittedly, some of these are just giant chunks of ice but one of them has a thicker atmosphere than Earth."

"So not all moons are like our Moon, then?" asked Alice.

"Not in the least. In the same way that the planets are different, so are their moons. The one circling Saturn, I mentioned, is called Titan. Its atmosphere is full of thick, orange clouds!"

"The rings," Emily Chickpea interrupted. "I thought we were going to talk about the rings!"

"Quite right!" said Miss Galaxy. "So we were. Any guesses what they're made out of?"

We all turned to Noel the Know-All.

"Ice," said Miss Galaxy dramatically. "Thousands and thousands of narrow rings made up of millions of pieces of ice."

"How small are these pieces of ice, Miss?" I asked. "The same size as the ice-cubes in my freezer?"

To my surprise, she nodded. "The smallest fragments are about the size of ice-cubes. The biggest would probably be the size of the Pickle Hill minibus."

"Imagine that floating in your drink!" said Max, beating me to it. The class laughed.

"I need a volunteer for this next part," said Miss Galaxy. I was up by her side with a "Me, Miss" before you could say "Royal Command Performance."

"Thank you, Bernie," she grinned. "But I think we'll have Alice." I sat down with a mutter of "Not fair!" and Alice came up to the front. "Now, be sure to stand very still," Miss Galaxy told her.

A moment later, I understood why she'd said that! She opened her handbag and pulled out a whole bunch of plastic hoops of different colours and sizes and began throwing them over Alice's head – smallest ones first. They didn't land on her shoulders but stayed at just about eye level. Suddenly Alice found her head slowly turning on her neck. I was now *glad* it wasn't me up there!

I WANT YOU TO IMAGINE THAT ALICE'S HEAD IS SATURN AND THE HOOPS ARE ITS RINGS. LIKE THE EARTH, SATURN HAS A TILTED AXIS.

BECAUSE OF THE ANGLE OF SATURN IN RELATION TO THE ANGLE OF THE EARTH, WE CAN SEE ALL OF THE RINGS, THROUGH A TELESCOPE, TWICE EVERY 29½ YEARS...

AND THE RINGS APPEAR TO DISAPPEAR COMPLETELY TWICE EVERY 29½ YEARS TOO, BECAUSE WE'RE LOOKING AT THE EDGE OF THE OUTERMOST RING AND IT'S NOTHING MORE THAN A THIN LINE!

I FEEL DIZZY!

Miss Galaxy thanked Alice and, a moment later, the hoops fell over her neck and on to her shoulders like a necklace.

Alice looked down at them. "They look pretty," she said, dizzily, and we all laughed!

"I can't use Alice's head for this next part," she said, "so I need another Saturn." She rummaged in her pocket and pulled out a spray can.

She sprayed it above her head with a hiss, and a ball of gas about the size of a baseball began to form in mid-air, and soon rings formed around it! Next, Miss Galaxy put away the can and carefully held the planet in her hands, the surface gases swirling between her fingers. It was a bit like someone holding a ball of mist.

"Because it's mainly made up of gas, Saturn has the lowest density of all the planets in our solar system. In other words, it's amazingly light for its size," she said. "Open the bottom doors of that cupboard will you, please, Alice? And pull out what's inside."

Alice did what she was told and found herself dragging out a large glass tank, full of water

"Having a bath, Miss?" I asked. "Going for a swim?"

Miss Galaxy chose to ignore my mega-brilliant wit. "If it was possible to drop any of the other eight planets into a tank of water

big enough to hold them, they would all sink.
Each and every one of them. But Saturn…"

The water splashed all over Alice, who looked
a bit soggy, but she didn't seem to mind.

As she pushed the tank back into the bottom of
the cupboard – not that it was there when I looked

at the end of the lesson – Miss Galaxy told us
more amazing facts about this amazing planet.

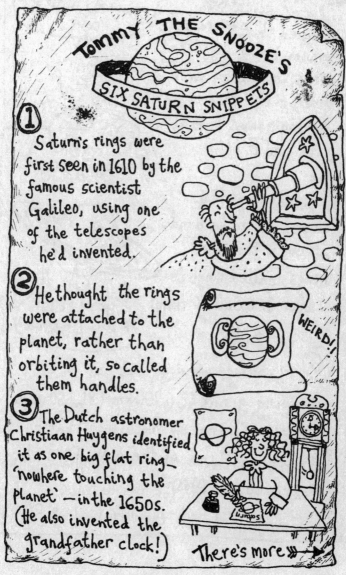

TOMMY THE SNOOZE'S

SIX SATURN SNIPPETS

1 Saturn's rings were first seen in 1610 by the famous scientist Galileo, using one of the telescopes he'd invented.

2 He thought the rings were attached to the planet, rather than orbiting it, so called them handles.

WEIRD!

3 The Dutch astronomer Christiaan Huygens identified it as one big flat ring – 'nowhere touching the planet' – in the 1650s. (He also invented the grandfather clock!)

There's more ≫➔

4 Later, scientists realized that there were a number of different rings, and they were given the rather boring names A, B, C, D, and E !!!

I GOT THE IDEA FROM MY ALPHABET SOUP.

5 These rings later turned out to be bands of even thinner rings, called ringlets — over 100,000 of them!

HEY! LET'S FORM A BAND!

6 The rings stretch out for a whopping great 136,200 km (84,550 miles) from the centre of Saturn. That's almost a third of the way from the Earth to the Moon!

Tommy Harte, at the very back of 5B!

"How do we know all this, Miss?" asked Noel the Know-All. "It's not as if anyone's ever set foot on Saturn."

Miss Galaxy gave him one of those funny looks which suggested that she had a picnic on the planet every weekend. Come to think of it, maybe she really *did* have a picnic on the planet every weekend. I was about to ask her what effect Saturn's atmosphere had on a cold hot-dog when she answered Noel's question.

"We know from *Pioneer 11* and *Voyagers 1* and *2*," she said. "All three are uncrewed US spacecraft which have flown near Saturn and taken lots of pictures and recorded lots of important information."

"Of course, Saturn isn't the only planet with rings," said Miss Galaxy. "Uranus – the next planet along as you fly from the Sun – has ten rings. Uranus is an odd planet because it's tilted on its side … and, before anyone asks, it has 15 moons. Shall we go and visit it?"

We didn't take much persuading. Our "Yes!" was deafening … and we were strapped in our chairs and ready for lift off before the ringing in my ears had even had a chance to stop!

"Can we actually land on Uranus, or is it another gassy ball?" asked Noel the Know-All. I was going to say something about *him* being a gassy ball, but decided that would be RUDE, so said nothing…

"With Uranus, pressure has turned much of the gas to liquid," said Miss Galaxy, floating in front of us because she wasn't strapped in and we'd blasted free of the Earth's gravitational pull. "The surface is covered in water."

THERE'S NO DRY LAND. ONE DAY, PERHAPS, A CRAFT WILL LAND AND SAIL ON IT, BUT TAKING OFF AGAIN COULD BE A PROBLEM.

"What we'll try to do is to land on one of the moons. I think Miranda will be our best bet … a very interesting place it is too!"

No sooner had Miss Galaxy said "Miranda" than the girls went: "Oooh!" I thought that they were oooh-ing at the pretty name, or something girlie like that, but then I realized that they were oooh-ing at what they could see outside the window!

There was cold, blue Uranus, with its rings running top to bottom rather than around the middle. Now I could see what Miss Galaxy meant about it being on its side.

She pulled herself over to her chair, did a slow-motion somersault and landed perfectly in the seat, strapping herself in position, ready for landing.

"I know we got here in next to no time with a little Pickle Hill know-how," she said, "but Uranus is so far away from Earth that it's very difficult to see without a telescope. Although it was discovered by a man named William Herschel back in 1781, we knew very little about it until the uncrewed probe *Voyager 2* came along... Ah! There's Miranda."

Miss Galaxy punched in a few codes on her control pad, and we lurched to the left. Lucky we were strapped in, or we'd have all ended up in a heap somewhere. I looked out of the window at our target: the moon, Miranda. It was absolutely covered in giant grooves and scratches. I don't really know how to describe it really. Nothing looked flat or smooth.

Moments later, we came in to land.

"This time, your special Pickle Hill Primary patented *Anti-Graviton* boots will make sure that none of you go leaping about on this moon, and you'll soon find out why! So get those boots and space suits on, then follow me."

Ten minutes later, we were out on the surface.

94

THERE ARE TWO MAIN THEORIES ON HOW THEY FORMED. ONE IS THAT THERE WAS ICE INSIDE THE MOON THAT MELTED AND MADE THESE PATTERNS...

ANOTHER IS THAT MIRANDA WAS HIT BY A METEORITE AND BADLY DAMAGED, AND THAT THIS IS A KIND OF HEALED WOUND WHERE IT RE-FORMED.

WAIT, YOU THREE! IT'S DANGEROUS!

It's hard to describe what me, Dripping and Max – yes, it was us three – felt as we stood on the edge of that cliff we'd so nearly fallen off. It wasn't just a long way down it was a *looooooooooooong* way down. We weren't just high up we were … we were… Well, put it this way, Noel the Know-All found out afterwards that Uranus's smallest moon, Miranda, is famous for two things: those grooves like racecourse tracks and that terrifying, knee-knocking, heart-pounding, sick-making cliff!!!

In fact, that cliff is so tall that it makes Mount Everest look like a little baby! It's so tall that, if it was on Earth, it'd not only get in the way of aeroplanes but even the space shuttle as it tried to orbit the planet! It's B-I-G … and I'm just glad we stopped running in time, even though I'm pretty sure Miss Galaxy wouldn't have let anything bad happen to us.

It was quiet as our classroom spacecraft headed off once more. There were groans of "Not back to Pickle Hill already!" but we were in for another surprise.

"Indeed not," said Miss Galaxy. "Seeing as we've come this far, I thought we might swing by the second-to-last planet in our solar system … which is?"

"Neptune!" said Sunita and Noel at exactly the same time.

Miss Galaxy nodded. "You've time to make a few notes on your digi-pads before we arrive."

"What are digi-pads?" asked Alice.

"These are," said Miss Galaxy and, at that precise moment, some electronic pads and special "pens" appeared in front of us.

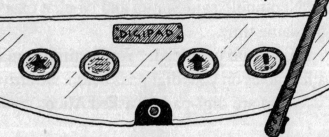

NEPTUNE by Noel O'Neill

- It's the eighth planet from our sun.
- It's circled by four rings.
- It has a number of moons, one of which – Triton – is the coldest place in our solar system.
- Neptune was discovered in 1846.
- Seen through a telescope, it's very small and very blue.
- People used to think that Neptune and Uranus were alike. They were called "The Twin Planets".
- Once "Voyager 2" had passed both planets (Uranus in 1986 and Neptune in 1989), scientists realized weather on Neptune was much worse: violent winds and "the spots".

DGTAD

"What are these spots then, Miss Galaxy?" I asked. "Chickenpox?"

Miss Galaxy tried not to smile, but I could see she thought it was funny. "No, Bernie," she said.

"Are they like the Great Red Spot on Jupiter?" Sunita suggested.

"Yes, that's right," said Miss Galaxy.

"Spot on!" I laughed.

"They're storms," Miss Galaxy continued. "The most famous ones were named the Great Dark Spot and the Scooter. They raged for hundreds of years. The Great Dark Spot was clearly seen in 1989 by *Voyager 2*, but had disappeared by the time the Hubble telescope studied Neptune in 1994 … but, by then, a new one had appeared." She pointed out of the window.

THAT SPOT THERE IS A STORM.

IT LOOKS LIKE A BRUISE!

"Aren't we going to stop off at Neptune?" asked Emily Chickpea, sounding a bit disappointed.

"Great idea," said Max. "Then we could all get blown to pieces in a choice of storms."

"Better still, let's stop off at its moon, Triton, and freeze to death!" I suggested.

"Interesting though it would be to visit both places," said Miss Galaxy, pretending to take us seriously, "I'm afraid it's time for us to get back to Pickle Hill! I'm supposed to be refereeing a basketball match a little later." Her eyes twinkled.

I wondered whether she ever got mistaken for the ball.

"Please make extra-sure you're strapped in properly," she went on. "Because I don't want us to be late, I'm going to have to fly this thing extra fast."

She punched in a few commands on her teacher's desk control panel. "We need to be back in five ... four ... three ... two ... one ... zero!"

There was a loud THUD and we were all back in our ordinary seats in our ordinary classroom with an ordinary view out of the window ... except we felt a little sh-sh-shaky!

"Well," said Miss Galaxy, straightening her hair. "Home sweet home! See you all next lesson!" With that, she waddled off.

Pluto, satellites, space stations and shuttles

The next morning came, and Miss Galaxy waddled back into 5B. "Hello, everyone," she said. "Today is our last lesson on our solar system." There were groans all round. "And we're going to kick off by looking at the planet furthest from the Sun."

As she said the words "kick off" she dropped an orange and kicked it high above our heads. Instead of splattering everywhere, covering us with pith, pips, skin and orange juice – which is what would've happened if I'd done that – it spun above our heads like a tiny planet.

"Imagine this orange is Pluto, the smallest planet

in our solar system by a long way," said Miss Galaxy, and the orbiting orange shrank and shrank and shrank until we could barely see it. "If the Earth was the size of a billiard ball, Pluto would be about as big as a knot in a piece of thread!"

She then had us write down some other pretty amazing facts.

by Emily

Bernie said Pluto was named after the Walt Disney dog. (I love dogs.) But it wasn't really. The planet was named after Pluto, the Roman god of the underworld.

Pluto wasn't discovered until the 20th century. It was found in 1930 by an American astronomer called Clyde Tombaugh.

Pluto definitely has at least one moon. It wasn't discovered until 1978 and then someone called it Charon.

The name Charon goes well with the name Pluto because, in Greek myths, Charon was the ferryman who rowed the souls of the dead across the River Styx to the underworld ruled by Pluto.

Charon is a very big moon compared to Pluto which it's orbiting.

Pluto has a core of rock, covered with ice and a frozen gas called methane.

Some people used to think that there must be a large planet beyond Neptune. It was referred to as "Planet X" and tiny Pluto was discovered during the search for it. (This got all the boys in the class really excited!) There's no real evidence that Planet X exists.

104

"Remember how we talked about gravity pulling objects down to Earth, and how much lighter you all felt on the Moon because gravity isn't so strong there?" said Miss Galaxy.

We nodded. "Well, it's the gravity of the planets that keep their moons orbiting them, and the gravity of our sun which keeps the planets pulled towards – and orbiting – it.

"By watching the way the distant planets move around in relation to each other, some people thought that there was another source of gravity –"

"And that source might have been another big planet," Noel interrupted.

"So now we've looked at all the planets in our solar system, what next?" asked Dave Horris. "A game of football?" Dave's football crazy.

Miss Galaxy frowned. "We could do ... but, first, I thought you might like to take a look at some of the other things that have either been up in space or are still up there. Human-made things, such as probes, satellites –"

"Space stations and the shuttle!" added a rather excited Emily Chickpea.

"Exactly," nodded Miss Galaxy. "Neptune, the furthest planet we can be sure of existing in our solar system, was visited by the unmanned probe *Voyager 2* in 1989. It set off back in 1977, so that was quite a journey."

"Was it un*wo*manned too?" asked Sunita.

"A good point!" grinned Miss Galaxy. "When experts use the term 'unmanned' they really mean 'un*hu*manned' – uncrewed, that is. In other words no people on board. Such probes don't carry people, just equipment which beams information back down to Earth."

"The probe that's been nearest to the Sun is *Mariner 10*, which also passed Mercury three times to gather scientific information. Then there's all that other human-made hardware up there, such as communication satellites so that we can talk to each other across the globe without telephone cable."

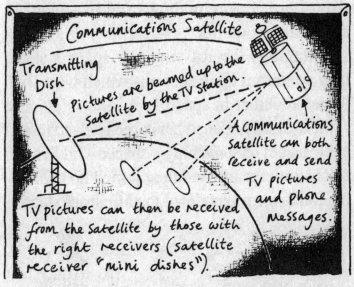

Communications Satellite

Transmitting Dish →

Pictures are beamed up to the satellite by the TV station.

A communications satellite can both receive and send TV pictures and phone messages.

TV pictures can then be received from the satellite by those with the right receivers (satellite receiver "mini dishes").

"Which was the first satellite?" Max asked.

"*Sputnik 1*," said Miss Galaxy. "It was launched by the Russians on 4th October 1957 – three-and-a-half years before the first human was launched into space, and more than ten years before a human set foot on the Moon. It caused a sensation! Science fiction had suddenly become science fact."

"With all the 'manned' space stations and space shuttles we have today, it's hard to imagine what an advance *Sputnik* seemed then."

"What do space stations look like?" asked Max. "If it's hard for a rocket to break free from Earth's gravity, how could a great big space station do it?"

"Like this, the Russian *Mir* space station, they were sent up in sections which were then joined together in space."

Miss Galaxy opened her carpetbag and tossed a few pieces of something – shaped a bit like loo rolls – into the air, and they joined up in slow-motion to form a model of the *Mir* space station!

The classroom became absolutely silent – as silent as space, where there's no air to carry sound – and the room darkened. All I could see were the segments joining together.

Now the Russian space station was complete. We all gasped. An American space shuttle had flown into view and was now docking with the station! It all seemed so real.

"The *Mir* space station crashed, though, didn't it?" asked Noel, excitedly.

"Yes, though there was no one in it any more, and this was after years of good service orbiting Earth. Most of it burnt up as it re-entered the Earth's atmosphere, but the few pieces which were left crashed. That was as recently as 2001." Miss Galaxy wobbled with enthusiasm.

"That was the same year that the first space tourist went into orbit, wasn't it?" asked Sunita, who had turned out to be a bit of a space buff.

"Well done. Yes it was," said Miss Galaxy.

HIS NAME WAS DENNIS TITO. HE WAS AN AMERICAN MILLIONAIRE AND THE FIRST PERSON TO PAY FOR A TRIP INTO SPACE JUST FOR THE FUN OF IT.

"He went on a Russian mission to the International Space Station, which is owned by lots of different countries, and agreed to pay extra for anything he broke, too!"

"Were you the first school teacher sent on a space mission, Miss?" asked Max.

Miss Galaxy shook her head. "No, sadly, the first teacher was an American lady called Christa McAuliffe. She was picked from hundreds for a place on a shuttle flight. Unfortunately, the space shuttle *Challenger* blew up 73 seconds after take off, in January 1986, with her and six other crew members on board, and they were all killed."

The model space station and space shuttle melted away to nothing and the classroom was bright again. Miss Galaxy sat behind her desk, looking very serious. "It's important to remember that, throughout the short history of human space exploration, there have been a number of tragic accidents. People have lost their lives in the effort to further our knowledge and interest in space. In this instance, the design fault in the space shuttles was corrected and they've been flown in many safe missions since."

"They sure have," said a voice, and there, once again, was the astronaut, hovering above our heads!

HI, YOU GUYS. REMEMBER ME?

"The space shuttle may *look* like an ordinary plane, and *land* like an ordinary plane, but how it takes off sure is a different matter," he said, floating towards the board behind Miss Galaxy.

Instead of hitting it, though, he somehow drifted *into* the board and, in a blink, he was standing in front of a space shuttle. It was as if we were looking through a window on to a launch pad!

ONCE THE FUEL TANK IS EMPTY, IT'S SET FREE IN SPACE.

INSIDE THE SHUTTLE, THERE'S ROOM FOR SEVEN OF US GUYS AND GALS. MOST EXPERIMENTS HAPPEN IN THE PAYLOAD BAY, WHICH CAN OPEN INTO SPACE.

WE OFTEN GET ABOUT IN ONE OF THESE, A "MANNED MANOEUVRING UNIT".

WE CALL THIS LITTLE BABY THE "FLYING ARMCHAIR".

The astronaut pressed one of the controls on his flying armchair and flew it straight through the board and above our heads. The board itself was as empty as space!

"Bye-byeeee!" he cried, and was gone. Just like that. Here one moment and then … *not*!

"Oh dear," said Miss Galaxy, looking at her watch. "I'm afraid we're out of time. Perhaps I'd better squeeze in another lesson on space tomorrow, after all."

We cheered.

At that exact moment, the bell for the end of the lesson rang and Miss Galaxy *floated* – yes floated – out of the door, spinning slowly as she went!

SEE YOU ALL TOMORROW... DIFFERENT TIME, SAME PLANET!

A fantastic finale!

Miss Galaxy's lesson was the last one before lunch the next day. When we walked into 5B, all our desks and chairs had gone. In their place there were large cushions for each of us.

RIGHT EVERYONE. LIE ON THE FLOOR AND LOOK UP AT THE CEILING.

The room went dark, and a million stars began to twinkle up above. I could hear everyone gasp … including me!

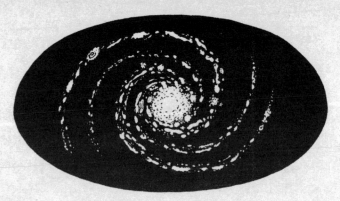

"Our solar system – with the Sun, nine planets and all those moons we've been looking at these past few days – is just one of billions of other solar systems in our galaxy, which is called the Milky Way," she explained. "That's what you're looking at now. Each of those twinkles of light is a star, and each of those stars is a…?"

"Sun!" we shouted.

"Good, and orbiting around each of these suns could be other planets, making up the other…?"

"Solar systems!"

"Excellent… Then you have to remember that the Milky Way is just one of many galaxies in the Universe, so there are countless stars and solar systems. The planet Earth is just a tiny part of something very big which began with the Big Bang 10 to 20 billion years ago!"

"What's the Big Bang?" asked Emily Chickpea. Drat! She got there first.

The image above us went black.

"Imagine all the matter – every planet, everything – and all the energy in the entire Universe packed together in a tiny space smaller than this ball … at temperatures so high even the most imaginative of us could never imagine them!" We watched a ball form above us.

THE BALL WAS SMALLER THAN AN ATOM, AND DENSER, CONTAINING MORE MATTER THAN THE LAWS OF PHYSICS CAN EXPLAIN...

"No one can fully understand the moment of the very beginning of the Big Bang, but we know what happened afterwards. There was a huge explosion and the Universe went from the size of an atom to the size of a beach ball in a split second… There were many weird and wonderful changes in forces including the creation of gravity. For a few million years, the Universe got bigger and bigger and bigger, and then the first stars probably began

117

to twinkle, with planets, trapped by their gravity, orbiting them…"

I wish I could draw you a picture of what we saw happening in front of our eyes – up there on the ceiling of 5B – as Miss Galaxy described all this. It was amazing … it was brilliant. But even Alice, with her best coloured crayons (and she's really good at art, especially horses) couldn't hope to draw the incredible things we'd just witnessed.

"I thought it would be a good idea if I got one of the world's greatest astronomers to come and explain a bit more about it," said Miss Galaxy. "So I asked Mrs Merlin, the headteacher, to arrange it. He should be here in five, four, three, two, one –"

There was a knock on the door, the classroom became bright again and we found ourselves sitting at our desks. The cushions had disappeared.

"Come in!" said Miss Galaxy, and a tall man with a hooded robe entered the room. He was weird-looking – even Miss Galaxy later said that he was "quite a sight" – and not the egghead scientist we were expecting.

Suddenly, Miss Galaxy let out a short burst of laughter. "I see what's happened!" she said. She opened the door with one hand and put her arm around the stranger's back with the other, steering him towards the doorway. "Thank you and goodbye. We don't need your doom and gloom around here!" She chuckled.

With the doom-and-gloom merchant out of the way, Miss Galaxy turned to us. "Mrs Merlin must have got into a bit of a muddle," she said. "That man certainly wasn't an astronomer. Can anyone tell me what he was."

"In need of a good smile!" I laughed.

"A soothsayer?" Sunita suggested.

"An astrologer?" said Noel the Know-All.

The class genius was – no surprises or prizes – right.

"Exactly! Well done," said Miss Galaxy and she wrote on the board:

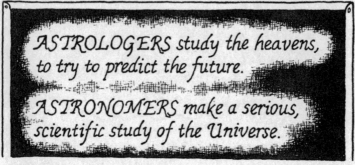

ASTROLOGERS study the heavens, to try to predict the future.

ASTRONOMERS make a serious, scientific study of the Universe.

"In the old days, many people thought that by studying the position of various planets, the Sun and the Moon in relation to certain constellations – and, before you ask, Bernie, that simply means groups of stars – they could find good omens and bad omens.

That way they could predict the outcomes of battles and things like that."

"I thought astrology was all about horoscopes, the signs of the zodiac and all that: Taurus the Bull, Cancer the Crab, Mickey the Mouse –" I said.

"My nan reads her horoscope everyday," said Dripping.

"The signs get their names from the constellations which appear at different times of year in the night sky," Miss Galaxy explained.

"Do you believe in all that hocus pocus?" asked Noel.

"I do not," said Miss Galaxy. "It's not a true science full of proven facts, like astronomy. Now, 5B, as this really is my last lesson with you on space, I've saved the best until last. The wonderful world of BLACK HOLES!"

THEY HAVE THEM ON TELLY! THEY'RE SOMETIMES CALLED WORMHOLES, AND THEY'RE REALLY GOOD SHORT-CUTS TO OTHER GALAXIES, AND SOME PEOPLE THINK YOU COULD USE THEM TO TIME TRAVEL AND –

"Thank you, Bernie!" said Miss Galaxy, very loudly. I'd got a bit over-enthusiastic! "Now, here are a few *facts*!"

Here are my notes on what she said. (Excellent handwriting, huh?)

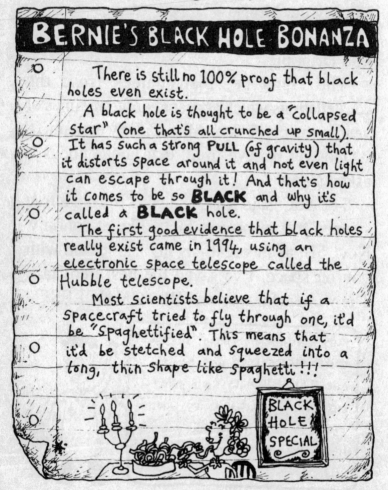

BERNIE'S BLACK HOLE BONANZA

- There is still no 100% proof that black holes even exist.
- A black hole is thought to be a "collapsed star" (one that's all crunched up small). It has such a strong **PULL** (of gravity) that it distorts space around it and not even light can escape through it! And that's how it comes to be so **BLACK** and why it's called a **BLACK** hole.
- The first good evidence that black holes really exist came in 1994, using an electronic space telescope called the Hubble telescope.
- Most scientists believe that if a spacecraft tried to fly through one, it'd be "spaghettified". This means that it'd be stetched and squeezed into a long, thin shape like spaghetti !!!

BLACK HOLE SPECIAL

We all had a good laugh about the spacecraft being spaghettified. "So, Miss, if I fell through a black hole, I'd end up as spaghetti sauce!"

"Are you volunteering?" asked Miss Galaxy.

"Sure!" I joked … but then the board opened up into a great big gaping hole of nothingness… Me and my big mouth!

It's impossible to say what it felt like as I became longer and thinner and longer and thinner and the laughter and cheers of the rest of 5B filled my ears.

Just as my head was about to stretch and disappear into that nothingness – and good old Mary-Jane was up on her desk and shouting "Save him! Save him!" – Miss Galaxy somehow yanked me out and I found myself normal shape and size – but a little tingly all over – standing at the front of the class. I sat down on the floor with a bump.

After that, there was a chorus of "Miss! Miss? Can I have a go?" as everyone stampeded forward... Well, not quite everyone. Mandy Patterson stayed in her seat. I think she was worried that, because she's so small, she might fall in and never come out again. And Tommy the Snooze stayed put because ... well, he was asleep! (It's a real skill. Even the shouting didn't wake him!) But everyone else took their turn in being spaghettified, with Miss Galaxy spinning above them, somehow staying out of the pull of the mighty black hole!

WHO'S NEXT, OR ARE WE ALL DONE?

And, just as the last one of us who wanted to be spaghettified had been spaghettified, the bell rang for the end of the lesson.

"I hope you've enjoyed our quick spin around space these past few days," said Miss Galaxy, coming in to land. "What part did you like best, 5B?"

Miss Galaxy put her hand up for silence. "Well, you'd better not be late for lunch," she said with a mischievous grin, "so here's something to help you all on your way!"

There was a whirring sound and we suddenly found that our desk chairs had turned into the flying armchairs – the "manned manoeuvring units" used by astronauts. It was a real shock for Tommy the Snooze, who woke up with a jolt to find himself hovering.

I'll bet you don't get lessons like these at your school, do you?